JULES FEIFFER

The EXPLAINERS

"I want to make this clear ..."
DWIGHT D. EISENHOWER

GIBBLE GABBLE GIBBLE GABBLE GIBBLE GABBLE GIBBLE GABBLE GIBBLE

McGRAW-HILL BOOK COMPANY, INC.

New York   Toronto   London

THE EXPLAINERS

First Edition
20369

The author wishes to thank *The Village Voice,*
Playboy magazine, The Hall Syndicate, Inc.,
and *The London Observer* for permission to reprint
the strips in this book.

PRETTY
SOON
I'LL
HAVE
TO
GET
UP.

IT'S NOT **HEALTHY** TO LIE HERE! GOT TO AROUSE MYSELF! GOT TO GET **INVOLVED!** **NOW! RIGHT NOW!**

OR AM I RATIONALIZING?

PERHAPS I DON'T **REALLY** WANT TO GET UP. PERHAPS I FEEL THAT I HAVE, AT LAST, FOUND MY ROLE.

OR PERHAPS THOUGH LYING HERE ATTRACTS ME, GETTING UP **ALSO** ATTRACTS ME— HENCE MY INDECISION —

SO THE **REAL** ISSUE IS NOT GETTING UP OR LYING DOWN. THE **REAL** ISSUE IS HOW DO I **HONESTLY** FEEL ABOUT EITHER MOVE —

BECAUSE WITHOUT FULLY
UNDERSTANDING MY
MOTIVATIONS, HOW CAN
EITHER ACT HAVE ANY
MEANING FOR ME?

NOW I MUST QUESTION
MYSELF **RELENTLESSLY.**
MY PATH IS CLEAR—

I MUST DIG!
I MUST PROBE!

PRETTY SOON I'LL HAVE
TO START PROBING—

I'LL COUNT TO THREE.

I'M SORRY
ABOUT THE
BONUS, HOWARD

WE'VE ALL BEEN PLEASED
WITH YOUR WORK THIS
PAST YEAR. IF ANYONE
DESERVED A BONUS,
YOU CERTAINLY DID.

BUT YOU KNOW THE COMPANY
POLICY AS WELL AS I DO. ALL
PERSONNEL WHO JOINED THE
FIRM AFTER JANUARY 15th
OF THE PRECEDING YEAR
ARE INELIGIBLE.

AND WE BOTH
KNOW THAT
YOU CAME TO
WORK ON
JANUARY **20**th
HOWARD.

NOW, OF COURSE IF **I** PERSONALLY HAD THE SAY, I'D GIVE IT TO YOU! I'D SET A **PRECEDENT**. *THE HELL WITH IT!*

BUT I'M ONLY THE PRESIDENT OF THE COMPANY, HOWARD. THERE'S A WHOLE BOARD OF DIRECTORS **I** GOT TO ANSWER TO.

THEY'D WANT TO KNOW WHO DOES THIS HOWARD THINK HE IS — A **PRIVILEGED CHARACTER?**

NOW YOU DON'T WANT PEOPLE THINKING YOU WANT TO BE TREATED LIKE A **PRIVILEGED CHARACTER**, HOWARD.

BUT YOU HAVE MY PERSONAL PROMISE THAT DURING THE COMING YEAR WE WILL FIND SOMEWAY OF MAKING IT UP TO YOU.

NOW AS SOON AS I GET OFF THE PHONE I WANT TO TALK TO YOU ABOUT YOUR LATENESS RECORD.

DON'T YOU SEE, HARRIET? HE'S TAKING AD**VANTAGE** OF YOU.

ALRIGHT, I **KNOW** ALL THAT. DON'T YOU THINK **I KNOW** ALL THAT?

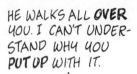

HE WALKS ALL **OVER** YOU. I CAN'T UNDERSTAND WHY YOU **PUT UP** WITH IT.

ALRIGHT, BUT THINK FOR A MINUTE WHAT A GOOD LOOKING FELLOW HE IS - AND HE HAS CHARM. AND HE'S A GOOD DANCER. AM I RIGHT?

RIGHT, BUT HE'S **STILL** TAKING ADVANTAGE OF YOU.

O.K. BUT BE HONEST, SYLVIA. WOULD HE HAVE **ANY** TROUBLE FINDING ANOTHER GIRL?

NONE. BUT HE'S **STILL** TAKING ADVANTAGE OF YOU.

SO IF HE CAN GET **ANY** GIRL HE **WANTS** AND **I'M** THE GIRL HE PICKS TO TAKE ADVANTAGE OF-

NOW LISTEN TO ME **ALWAYS** LOOK OUT FOR YOURSELF. YOU LOOK OUT TOO MUCH FOR THE **OTHER** FELLOW AND WHEN **HE GETS** TO THE TOP HE'LL ONLY KICK YOU IN THE TEETH FOR THANKS.

NOW **LISTEN** TO ME. LEARN TO BE WATCHFUL. NEVER TRUST ANYBODY — NOT EVEN ME! THE WORLDS OUT TO **GET YOU.**

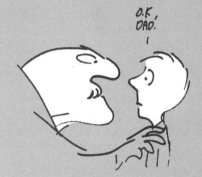

NOW LISTEN TO ME. DEVELOP SINCERITY. LEARN A STRONG HANDSHAKE AND A GOOD EYE STARE. ALWAYS BE ATTENTIVE TO STRANGERS. THEY MIGHT DO YOU SOME GOOD.

NOW LISTEN TO ME. DON'T **EVER** FEEL SORRY FOR YOURSELF. YOU'RE EATING GOOD AND YOU'VE ALWAYS GOT A CHANCE. WITH THE RIGHT MENTAL ATTITUDE YOU CAN TAKE **ANYBODY.**

NOW FOR CRYING OUT LOUD, **LISTEN** TO ME. DON'T DO FAVORS! DON'T BE A PATSY! THE **SMART** GUYS **LAUGH** AT THE NICE GUYS. NEVER EXPECT TOO MUCH AND YOU WON'T BE DISAPPOINTED.

WILL YOU **PLEASE** LISTEN TO ME. **NEVER** TALK POLITICS. YOU ONLY MAKE ENEMIES AND NOTHING **YOU'RE** GONNA SAY WILL EVER CHANGE THE WORLD.

C'MON NOW YOU'RE NOT **LISTENING** TO ME. RESPECT **EVERY** GIRL LIKE SHE WAS YOUR MOTHER. BUT WHEN YOU **GOT** TO FOOL AROUND DO IT OUT OF THE NEIGHBORHOOD. NEVER PLAY IN YOUR OWN BACKYARD

YESSIR, WE'LL PUT OUR HEADS TOGETHER AND MAKE A MAN OUT OF YOU. YOU LISTENING, BOY?

I USED TO BE
SUPERMAN

I USED TO GO RESCUING
PEOPLE ALL THE
HELL OVER THE
PLACE. WHERE-
EVER YOU
LOOKED
I WAS
SAVING
**SOME-
BODY**

THEN ONE DAY I
PULLED THIS
CHICK FROM
THE RIVER.
DO YOU
THINK
SHE
THANKED
ME?
NO!

SHE JUST WANTED TO
KNOW WHY I
HAD THIS
COMPULSION
TO RESCUE.

SHE ACCUSED ME OF DOUBTING MY MASCULINITY AND HENCE MY EXHIBITIONIST TENDENCIES. SHE WANTED TO KNOW WHY I DIDN'T SPEND MORE TIME **READING.**

SHE TOOK ONE LOOK AT MY CAPE AND SAID I WAS A LATENT TRANSVESTITE AND WHY WAS MY COSTUME SO SKIN TIGHT AND DID I RESCUE MORE **MEN** THAN **WOMEN-**

I TRIED TO TELL HER SHE SHOULDN'T JUDGE ME THE WAY SHE JUDGES EARTH PEOPLE. SHE JUST PATTED MY HEAD AND SMILED.

SO AFTER A LOT OF ARGUMENT BACK AND FORTH, I FINALLY GOT HER TO ADMIT THAT ALTHOUGH I MIGHT NOT BE **SUPER,** I WAS A LOT BETTER THAN **AVERAGE.**

NOW I HAVE A REGULAR OFFICE JOB IN THE CITY AND A HOUSE IN THE SUBURBS. WE'RE BOTH **VERY** HAPPY.

YOU'RE NOT
PERFECTION.
YOUR COLOR
ISN'T RIGHT
AND YOU'RE
TOO
SMALL.

YOU'RE NOT PERFECTION.
YOUR COLOR ISN'T
RIGHT- YOU'RE TOO
SMALL AND YOU'RE
BEGINNING TO FADE.

YOU'RE
NOT
PERFECTION.—

AND YOU'RE
NOT
PRETENTIOUSLY
LARGE —

AND YOU'RE
OBVIOUSLY
QUITE DELICATE—
WHICH
CONNOTATES
BREEDING —

AND BESIDES
IT'S GETTING
DARK.

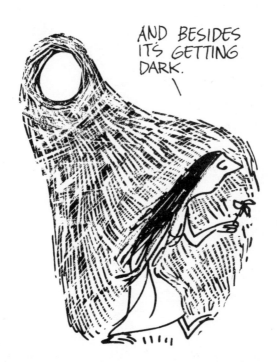

ALL RIGHT, EVERYONE, LETS JOIN HANDS!

WHO'S THAT?

THE VOICE OF TOGETHER- NESS

LETS GO, GANG! LETS ALL HOP TO OUR FEET AND DANCE!

TELL HER TO SHUT UP.

SHE DOESN'T KNOW HOW.

COME ON, GUYS AND GALS! HIGH, HIGH, HIGH ON YOUR TOES! ONE AND TWO AND ONE AND TWO —

DOES SHE ACTUALLY FEEL THIS ACCOMPLISHES ANYTHING?

SHE THINKS SHE'S SPREAD- ING LOVE.

I SEE TWO STRAGGLERS! UP, UP ON YOUR TOES, STRAGGLERS!

SHE OFFENDS ME!

SHALL WE TAKE A STAND?

JOIN HANDS,
STRAGGLERS!
HIGH, HIGH ON
YOUR TOES!

I'M NOT
SURE I
WANT TO
HURT
HER.

SHE'S
ONLY
DOING
WHAT SHE
FEELS
IS
RIGHT.

COME NOW, STRAGGLERS!
DON'T SPOIL EVERYONE'S
GOOD TIME!

SHE
WOULDN'T
UNDERSTAND
OUR
POINT
ANY-
HOW.

SHE
MIGHT
CRY.

HANDS HIGH!
UP! UP! UP!

WHY
CAUSE
TROUBLE?

SHE
DOES
HAVE A
GOOD
HEART.

ONE AND TWO
AND ONE AND
TWO AND—

IT'S WE WHO
HAVE INSIGHT
WHO MUST
MAKE THE
CONCESSIONS.

ROBERT'S MO-THER!

1.

ROBERT'S MOTHER,
COULD ROBERT
COME OUT TO THE
WADING POOL
AND WADE?

2.

ROBERT HONEY, THERE'S
THAT NICE LITTLE
GLORIA OUTSIDE AND
SHE'S ASKED TO GO
WADING WITH YOU.

I DON'T
WANT
TO GO
WADING.

3.

DON'T BE STUBBORN,
ROBERT SWEETIE.
YOU **KNOW** ONCE
YOU GET IN THE
WATER YOU ALWAYS
LOVE IT.

I **DON'T**
LOVE IT.
I ALWAYS
GET **PUSHED**.
EVERYBODY
PUSHES
ME!

4.

ROBERT DARLING,
THEY'RE PUSHING
YOU FOR **FUN**.
THAT'S ONLY **FUN**
WHEN THEY PUSH
YOU.

I DON'T
LIKE
BEING
PUSHED.
THEY
DUNK
ME.

5.

ROBERT LOVELY, YOU'VE GOT TO HAVE A SENSE OF **HUMOR** ABOUT THESE THINGS. THEY'RE **BIGGER** THAN YOU ARE SO THEY **DUNK** YOU.

YEAH. I DON'T LIKE IT.

6.

BUT, ROBERT SUGAR, THEN **YOU'LL** BE BIGGER THAN SOME-BODY **ELSE** AND YOU'LL PUSH **HIM**. THAT'S HAVING A SENSE OF **HUMOR**.

CAN I PUSH GLORIA?

7.

GLORIA IS A **GIRL**, ROBERT BABY. IT IS NOT BEING GENTLE-MANLY WHEN YOU PUSH A GIRL. IF I HEAR OF YOU PUSHING A GIRL I'LL MAKE YOU **REGRET** IT.

SHE'S MY SIZE.

8.

ROBERT DEAREST, MOTHER IS JUST SENDING YOU WADING. I SWEAR, SWEETHEART, IT'S **ONLY** WADING.

DON'T, MAMMA! I'LL GET **PUSHED!**

9.

MY KID. HE ACTS LIKE HAVING FUN IS A DEATH SENTENCE.

10.

PUT ON YOUR SHOES — I'LL WALK YOU TO THE SUBWAY.

YOU NEEDN'T BOTHER. I'VE NEVER MET ANYONE SO CRUDE IN MY LIFE.

YEH, CRUDE — NOW PUT ON YOUR SHOES — I'LL WALK YOU TO THE SUBWAY.

YOU WANT EVERYTHING YOUR **OWN** WAY! **YOU'RE SPOILED!**

YEH, SPOILED — NOW PUT ON YOUR SHOES — I'LL WALK YOU TO THE SUBWAY

I DON'T LIKE BEING **PUSHED** INTO THINGS. I NEED A **LITTLE** TIME YOU KNOW!

YEH, TIME — NOW PUT ON YOUR SHOES — I'LL WALK YOU TO THE SUBWAY.

I MEAN — WE'VE HARDLY EVEN **TALKED**.

YEH, TALK — NOW PUT ON YOUR SHOES — I'LL WALK YOU TO THE SUBWAY.

YOU'RE CERTAINLY ANXIOUS TO GET RID OF ME.

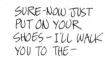

ONCE I
WANTED
TO BE A
WRITER.

BUT I
DEVELOPED
WRITER'S
BLOCK.

SO INSTEAD
I DECIDED
TO BE A
PAINTER.

BUT I
DEVELOPED
PAINTER'S
BLOCK.

SO I TURNED
MY TALENTS
TO THE
THEATRE.

BUT I
DEVELOPED
THEATRE
BLOCK.

SO I THOUGHT IT ALL THROUGH AND DECIDED MY TROUBLE WAS **OVER-SPECIALIZATION.** I SHOULD **DIVERSIFY.**

SO I TOOK UP MUSIC, MODERN DANCE, WOOD SCULPTURE, AND POETRY.

BUT I DEVELOPED A MUSIC BLOCK, A MODERN DANCE BLOCK, A WOOD SCULPTURE BLOCK AND A POETRY BLOCK.

SO I GAVE IT ALL UP AND TOOK A JOB AS A RECEPTIONIST.

AND SOMEHOW I'M NOT BLOCKING ANYMORE.

O.K. YOU WANNA KNOW WHAT'S CAUSING JUVEN-ILE DELINQUENCY? THE **BREAKDOWN** OF THE SYSTEM. **THAT'S** WHAT'S CAUSING JUVEN-ILE DELINQUENCY.

LOOK, YOU'RE LIVING IN A WORLD WHERE Y'GOTTA GO WITH THE SYSTEM. THAT'S **CIVILIZATION!** IF YOU GOT NO SYSTEM, YOU GOT NO RULES. IF YOU GOT NO RULES — **WHAMMY!** ALL HELL BREAKS LOOSE.

NOW **WE** GOT A SYSTEM. OUR SYSTEM IS **CORRUPTION.** IT WAS LIKE THAT WHEN **I** WAS A KID. IT'S LIKE THAT **TODAY.** YOU UNDERMINE A KID'S FAITH IN CORRUPTION AND YOU'RE ASKING FOR TROUBLE.

SO **MAKE** A BIG STINK OUTA POLICE PAYOFFS AND BUTCHER'S FAT THUMBS. THATS NOTHING **NEW.** KIDS'VE KNOWN THAT STUFF FOR **YEARS!**

ONLY **THEY**
NEVER KNEW
IT WAS
WRONG.

YOU TELL KIDS THE VALUES
THEY GREW UP WITH ARE
WRONG AND THEY LOSE
RESPECT FOR THE **SYSTEM**.
THEY GO OFF THEIR NUT.

O.K - SO YOU ARREST A
FEW PEOPLE. WHADAYA
CHANGE? COPS **AIN'T** GON-
NA TAKE PAYOFFS?
LANDLORDS ARE GONNA
VOLUNTEER YOU REPAIRS?

LOOK- IT'S GONNA GO
ON **ANYHOW!** STOP
ALL THE SCREAMING!
LEGALIZE CORRUPTION!

GIVE OUR CHILDREN
BACK THEIR ROOTS.

"WHAT I BELIEVE"
-A COMPOSITION
FOR SIXTH GRADE
ENGLISH.

"BE WATCHFUL — OPPORTUNITY
MAY PRESENT ITSELF AT ANY
MOMENT. DON'T GET **TOO**
FAR AHEAD OF YOUR
COMPANIONS **TOO**
QUICKLY. "

" BE AGREEABLE — MAKE A
GOOD IMPRESSION ON
OTHERS. NEW FRIENDS
EQUAL NEW CONTACTS."

" BE CAUTIOUS - NO ONE IS
POPULAR WHEN HE'S WRONG.
COVER YOURSELF ON ALL BASES.
LET **OTHERS** GIVE THE
FIRST OPINION. "

BE INDUSTRIOUS —
DEVELOP A GOOD MEMORY.
NEW IDEAS ARE ALWAYS
IN DEMAND."

"BE MANEUVERABLE —
DON'T EVER LET THEM
KNOW WHAT YOU'RE
THINKING."

HOW DOES
IT SOUND,
DAD ?

HMMMM

I **THINK** THAT'S **ALMOST** IT.
WHY NOT LEAVE IT FOR A FEW
DAYS AND LET YOUR MOTHER
AND ME KICK IT AROUND.

LISTEN, LET'S BE **HONEST**! LET'S BE GROWN UP ABOUT IT! LET'S FACE **FACTS**!

SOME TELEVISION IS **MEDIOCRE**.

TO BE **BRUTALLY** FRANK, EVEN **I** DON'T LIKE ALL OF OUR NETWORK'S PROGRAMMING. **HELL**, WHY BEAT AROUND THE BUSH? SOME OF THESE SPONSORS ARE JUST NOT INTERESTED IN THE CREATIVE PROCESS.

IF YOU'LL FORGIVE MY BLUNDERING HONESTY, SOME ARE JUST OUT FOR THE **BUCK**! THAT'S STRICTLY OFF THE RECORD, MIND YOU.

I WON'T KID YOU, IT'S A **HARD** FIGHT! BUT I'LL BE TRUTHFUL- AS LONG AS I'M SITTING BEHIND THIS DESK I **STICK MY NECK OUT**! LET 'EM **FIRE** ME! I SAY WHAT I THINK.

WHAT THE HELL, I'LL TELL YOU THE UNVARNISHED, BRUTALLY, PERFECTLY HONEST TRUTH. WE GOT TO HIRE SOME GOOD WRITERS. GIVE 'EM A **CHANCE**. THEY MIGHT EVEN WORK OUT.

LISTEN—I DON'T SAY ROME CAN BE BUILT IN ONE NINETY-MINUTE TIME SLOT. WE GOT TO WORK **SLOW**. YOU CAN'T STUN THE TRADE WITH SUDDEN QUALITY.

WE'LL BEGIN WITH **LITTLE** THINGS. QUALITY STATION BREAKS. QUALITY TIME CHECKS. QUALITY WEATHER REPORTS. THIRTY SECONDS OF QUALITY **EVERY PROGRAMMING HOUR!**

WE WORK **QUIETLY** FROM THE INSIDE. WE EXPAND **LITTLE** BY **LITTLE**. SOON THE TRADE IS **RIDDLED THROUGH** WITH QUALITY AND DOESN'T EVEN KNOW IT.

ONCE WE GET THEM TO ACCEPT QUALITY AS BEING MEDIOCRE, WE'RE **IN**.

IT HASN'T ALWAYS BEEN EASY. ONCE I WAS ROTTEN.

I LOOKED ROTTEN. I THOUGHT ROTTEN. I COULD TELL BY THE WAY PEOPLE STARED AWAY FROM ME THAT THEY WERE THINKING - "THERE GOES A ROTTEN KID."

SO I DECIDED TO CONVERT. I STUDIED TO BE NICE.

AT FIRST IT WAS PURE AFFECTATION. OUTSIDE I DID FAVORS, LENT MONEY, SMILED A LOT. BUT INSIDE, I STAYED **ROTTEN**.

BUT GIVE NICENESS AN INCH AND IT TAKES A MILE. NICENESS RAN **AMOK** INSIDE OF ME. I BECAME A COMPULSIVE **DOLL**.

WHEN I CAME INTO A ROOM PEOPLE **CHEERED**. I GOT DEPEND-ENT ON IT. I GOT NICER AND **NICER**!

EVEN WHEN IT WASN'T NECESSARY I WAS NICE. GUYS WOULDN'T CURSE IN MY COMPANY, GIRLS BEGAN TO THINK OF ME AS A **FRIEND**. I GAVE MY MINISTER **GUILT** FEELINGS.

I TRIED TO CUT DOWN BUT I HAD LOST THE POWER OF CHOICE. I **WAS HOOKED ON NICE**!

DO YOU KNOW WHAT IT'S LIKE TO HAVE A FORTY POUND MONKEY ON YOUR BACK?

NOT THAT I'M COMPLAINING, MIND YOU.

USED TO GO TO
THE VAUDEVILLE
HOUSE - HEAR
A GOOD
RASTUS -
MANDY STORY.
EVERYONE
LOVED 'EM!
NOBODY
TOOK IT
WRONG.

TRY TO
TELL ONE
TODAY -
EVERYONE'S
OFFENDED.

USED TO GO
TO PARTIES -
STAYED UP ALL
NIGHT TELLING
HYMIE - ABIE
STORIES.
LAUGHED? WE
COULDA **DIED!**
IT WAS ALL
IN FUN.

TRY TO
TELL ONE
TODAY -
EVERYONE
GETS
OFFENDED.

USED TO GET TOGETHER AFTER A STAG MOVIE AND TELL MICK JOKES, CHINAMAN JOKES, POLACK JOKES, LIMEY JOKES, FROG JOKES— A **MILLION** LAUGHS!

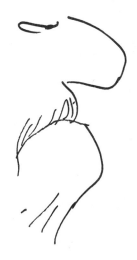

TRY TO TELL 'EM TODAY— YOU GET YOUR HEAD BUSTED.

USED TO DO THIS IMITATION OF A GUY WITH A BAD LEG. A **REGULAR RIOT!** TRY TO IMITATE A CRIPPLE TODAY— SEE WHAT IT GETS YOU!

HUMOR IS DEAD IN THIS COUNTRY.

I'LL
COMPROMISE.

TODAY'S BOOK IS A RATHER BULKY BUT PROMISING FIRST ATTEMPT BY AUTHOR OR AUTHORS UNKNOWN.

IT'S CALLED "THE BIBLE."

IT IS WRITTEN IN A NARRATIVE RATHER THAN INTROSPECTIVE STYLE WHICH MAY PERHAPS MAKE FOR QUICKER READING BUT LEAVES SOMETHING TO BE DESIRED ON THE LEVEL OF CHARACTER MOTIVATION.

IT PURPORTS TO BE A THEOLOGICAL AND HISTORICAL DOCUMENT, AND WHILE THIS REVIEWER DOES NOT QUESTION ITS SINCERITY, HE CAN ONLY REGRET THE PUBLISHER'S FAILURE TO INCLUDE A BIBLIOGRAPHY.

BUT THESE ARE MINOR CRITICISMS. ONE CAN NOT DENY THE POWER AND SWEEPING RANGE OF THE SUBJECT MATTER - (ONE MIGHT EVEN CALL IT EPIC) —

- THE SUBTLE ALLEGORICAL NUANCES TOUCHED, AT TIMES, WITH WHAT SEEMS TO BE AN ALMOST METAPHYSICAL INSIGHT! IT WILL UNDOUBTEDLY CAUSE CONTROVERSY IN THE LITERARY FIELD.

BUT THE AUTHORS, WHILE WRITING IN A QUASI-JOURNALISTIC FORM SHOW OCCASIONAL FLOURISHES OF STYLISTIC DARING WHICH MAKES ONE IMPATIENT TO VIEW THEIR LATER EFFORTS.

I SHALL AWAIT THEIR SECOND BOOK WITH GREAT INTEREST.

THE EVOLUTIONARY PROCESS IN GOVERNMENT CONTINUES. WE HAVE PASSED FROM FEUDALISM TO CAPITALISM. OUR CURRENT STAGE, AS WE ALL KNOW, IS **CORRUPTION.**

CORRUPTION AS A FORM OF GOVERNMENT IS, ITSELF, WITHIN VARYING STAGES OF DEVELOPMENT. IN THE SOVIET UNION, WHERE YOU HAVE THE "**STATE**" OR "**TRICKLE DOWN**" THEORY OF CORRUPTION, IT OPERATES WITH THE **MOST** EFFICIENCY.

IN OUR **OWN** COUNTRY WE ARE IN THE TRANSITIONAL, MORE DYNAMIC PHASE — **FREE FORM** CORRUPTION. IT IS AN UNPREDICTABLE PHASE BECAUSE IT CONTINUES, SELF CONSCIOUSLY, TO DENY ITS EXISTENCE IN FEAR THAT, WERE ITS **TRUE** NATURE MADE KNOWN, IT WOULD BE OVERTHROWN.

THEREFORE, IN LINE WITH THE CURRENT PRACTICES OF ENLIGHTENED LEADERSHIP, IT PUBLICLY **DEPLORES** WHAT IT PRIVATELY OWES ITS EXISTENCE TO.

AS PART OF THIS PHILOSOPHY IT OFFERS A REGULAR PROGRAM OF PLANNED EXPOSURES TO SATISFY THE PUBLIC'S APPETITE — A BUILDING INSPECTOR ONE MONTH, A CITY OFFICIAL ANOTHER MONTH — **ANYTHING** WHICH WILL MISDIRECT THE GAZE OF AN ANTI-CORRUPT CITIZENRY.

THUS THE PUBLIC IS ENCOURAGED TO THINK OF CORRUPTION AS AN UNWELCOME STRANGER IN ITS HOUSE RATHER THAN AS THE HOST.

IN THE MEANTIME, TO SOFTEN THE PUBLIC'S ANTI CORRUPTION NEO-IDEALISM, THERE WILL BE A GROWING LIST OF **PEER GROUP** EXPOSURES— PROMINENT PRIVATE CITIZENS, IMPORTANT BUSINESS LEADERS, LEADING INTELLECTUALS —

WITH SO MUCH CORRUPTION MADE SO APALLINGLY EVIDENT, PUBLIC RESPONSE WILL DEADEN AND WITHDRAW. ACCEPTANCE WILL SET IN. CORRUPTION'S TAKE OVER WILL BE **COMPLETE**.

IN EVERY SCHOOL IN THE LAND WILL BE ENGRAVED OUR **NEW** MORAL BANNER ———

"WHAT CAN YOU EXPECT? I'D DO IT MYSELF."

HELLO, IS THIS MR. MERGENDIELER? THIS IS MISS SACROSANCT OF THE TELEPHONE COMPANY, MR. MERGENDIELER. WHAT I'M CALLING ABOUT IS YOUR REQUEST FOR AN UNLISTED NUMBER.

1.

NOW ACCORDING TO OUR RECORDS, MR. MERGENDIELER, YOU ALREADY HAVE A PHONE WITH US. AND IT **IS** LISTED. NOW THE PHONE YOU WISH TO HAVE **UNLISTED** — IS THIS TO BE A **NEW** NUMBER OR THE NUMBER **NOW** LISTED?

2.

THE REASON I'M ASK-ING, MR. MERGENDIELER, IS THAT THERE WILL BE A **DELETION** CHARGE TO HAVE YOUR NAME REMOVED FROM THE LISTING ONCE IT'S ALREADY **THERE.** I'M **SURE** YOU CAN UNDER-STAND THE EXPENSE. EVERY NAME IN THE TELEPHONE BOOK WILL HAVE TO BE MOVED UP ONE.

3.

ON THE OTHER HAND, IF YOU TAKE A **NEW** PHONE THERE WOULD **NOT** BE THE DELETION CHARGE. HOWEVER, THERE **WOULD** BE AN **ANONYMITY** CHARGE TO KEEP YOUR NAME STRICKEN FROM THE ROLLS IN **EITHER** CASE.

4.

I SEE. WELL, BEFORE YOU HAVE YOUR PHONE TAKEN **OUT**, MR. MERGENDIELER, LET ME TELL YOU ABOUT OUR MONTHLY CHARGE FOR HOMES THAT ONCE PATRONIZED BUT HAVE SINCE REJECTED YOUR TELEPHONE COMPANY. THAT MEANS IF YOU EVER WANT A PHONE AGAIN YOU MUST PAY ARREARS.

5.

NOW ABOUT THAT NEW UNLISTED PHONE - I WONDER IF YOU'VE CONSIDERED HAVING **MORE** THAN ONE- IT COSTS SO LITTLE EXTRA TO HAVE AN EXTENSION, MR. MERGENDIELER. NOW WHAT **COLORS** WOULD YOU LIKE THEM IN?

6.

I SEE. I SEE. WELL, THERE'S **NO** NEED TO SCREAM, MR. MERGENDIELER. NO ONE IS **FORCING** YOU TO DO BUSINESS WITH US.

7.

YOU CAN ALWAYS GO TO ONE OF OUR COMPETITORS.

8.

THE MEETING OF THE "I'M JUST DOING MY JOB CLUB" WILL COME TO ORDER. WE WILL BEGIN WITH A REPORT FROM MEMBER ROCKWELL J.

I BEGAN AS A MONITOR IN GRAMMAR SCHOOL. WHEN I WAS CALLED DOWN FOR REPORTING MY CLASS MATES, I SIMPLY ANSWERED— "DON'T BLAME ME. I WAS **TOLD** TO DO IT.

PROMISING

VERY PROMISING.

LATER ON I WAS IN THE MILITARY SERVICE. IT WAS MY JOB TO CLASSIFY PERSONNEL. I DIDN'T **LIKE** TO SEND MEN TO WAR. BUT THOSE WERE MY **ORDERS**. I HAD NO CHOICE.

AFTER SERVICE I HAD TROUBLE FINDING MY NICHE. FOR AWHILE I WAS REALTY AGENT FOR A SLUM. THE TENANTS DIDN'T UNDERSTAND. I WAS JUST DOING WHAT I WAS HIRED TO DO.

REASONABLE!

QUITE REASONABLE!

RESPONSIBLE!

HIGHLY RESPONSIBLE!

NEXT I WENT TO WORK AS A WITNESS. I APPEARED BEFORE DOZENS OF CONGRESSIONAL COMMITTEES. I DIDN'T **LIKE** THE WORK. BUT I **HAD** TO DO WHAT I WAS BEING PAID FOR.

AND NOW I'VE REACHED THE **PINNACLE!** I'VE GONE TO WORK IN A STATE PRISON. I DON'T NECESSARILY BELIEVE IN CAPITAL PUNISHMENT BUT **SOMEONE** HAS TO PULL THE SWITCH.

OF COURSE **SOME** PEOPLE DON'T UNDERSTAND. THEY ASSOCIATE **ME** WITH THE WAY I MAKE A LIVING.

NEXT WE HEAR FROM MEMBER ARNOLD K. HE WILL SPEAK ON INTERCONTINENTAL BALLISTIC MISSILES.

SO I'M GOING OUT WITH THIS GIRL FOR THE FIRST TIME AND WE'RE GOING TO THE MOVIES AND, AS USUAL, I'M THROWING OUT MY BREAD CRUMBS.

AND SHE ASKS ME WHAT IS IT THAT I'M DOING AND I TELL HER THAT I'M THROWING OUT BREAD CRUMBS SO I CAN FIND MY WAY HOME BECAUSE I HAVE THIS BAD SENSE OF DIRECTION.

SO SHE LAUGHS LIKE IT'S A BIG JOKE AND I SAY I DON'T SEE WHY MY PERSONAL TROUBLES SHOULD MAKE SUCH A BIG JOKE.

AND THEN SHE SAID "LOOK- DON'T WORRY - I'LL TAKE YOU HOME!" SO I GOT MAD. I SAID "LOOK- WE EACH HAVE OUR OWN WAY OF FINDING OURSELVES. WHO IS TO SAY YOURS IS BETTER THAN MINE?"

AND SHE SAYS "YOU CAN'T MAKE A WHOLE LIFE'S PHILOSOPHY OUT OF BREAD CRUMBS". SO RIGHT OUT ON THE STREET WE HAD A FIGHT.

AND I GOT **SO** MAD I WALKED AWAY AND I COMPLETELY FORGOT TO FOLLOW MY BREAD CRUMBS.

AND AN AMAZING THING HAPPENED— I HAD NO TROUBLE GETTING HOME.

IT SEEMS TO MAKE MY WHOLE PAST LIFE INVALID.

YOU MISSED IT, HUH? IT WAS IN TWO PARTS ON "PLAYHOUSE 90." REALLY **WEIRD**.

I HAD TO LISTEN TO CHAMBER MUSIC. WHAT WAS IT ABOUT?

IT WAS SORT OF HARD TO TELL— **SPAIN** OR **MEXICO** OR SOMETHING— IT WAS ABOUT BLOWING UP A BRIDGE.

OH, WHAT YOU MEAN IS "BRIDGE ON THE RIVER KWAI." THAT WAS **ASIA**.

NO. THAT WASN'T IT. ALTHOUGH THAT'S PROBABLY WHERE THEY GOT THE IDEA. IT WAS SOME KIND OF **CIVIL WAR**— IN SPAIN I THINK.

OH, **YOU** MEAN IN THE **1800's**. I THINK I REMEMBER READING—

IT WASN'T! THEY HAD TANKS AND GUNS AND THIS AMERICAN, ROBERT JORDAN, GOES OVER AND JOINS THE REBELS.

WHAT WAS HE? A **MERCENARY** YOU KNOW, ARMIES AT ONE TIME WERE MADE UP OF MERCEN—

ACTUALLY, WE **FIRST** THOUGHT OF SENDING HIM TO "VILLAGE AND STREAM". I UNDERSTAND THEY'RE **VERY** GOOD FOR SENSITIVE CHILDREN.

BUT **THEN** WE HEARD THAT THEIR STUDENT SELECTION WAS ETHNICALLY NARROW AND WE **BOTH** FELT IT WAS IMPORTANT FOR HIS MULTI-CULTURAL EXPERIENCES TO HAVE THEIR LABORATORY TRYOUT AT THE **EARLIEST** POSSIBLE MOMENT.

SO WE ASKED **AROUND** AND HEARD ABOUT "COUNTY AND "HILLOCK". BUT UNFORTUNATELY THEY BELIEVE IN "PLANNED PERMISSIVENESS" AND "CONTROLLED OUTBURST," WHICH **BOTH** OF US FIND **TERRIBLY** DATED.

THEN WE BECAME INTRIGUED WITH "ROCK IN THE VALLEY" BECAUSE OF THEIR GROUP THERAPY PROGRAM FOR FOUR-YEAR-OLDS. BUT THEY INSISTED ON PARENTAL PARTICIP-ATION, AND **WHO** HAS THE TIME?

CONSEQUENTLY ALL THAT WAS LEFT WAS "DROP IN THE OCEAN" AND "CHICKEN IN THE BASKET," AND WHILE BOTH ARE, OF COURSE, FINE SCHOOLS **NEITHER** HAS THE RIGHT CONNECTION WITH HARVARD.

SO WE DECIDED TO HOLD HIM OUT OF SCHOOL FOR ANOTHER SIX MONTHS AND PUT OFF A DECISION TILL HE'S TWO.

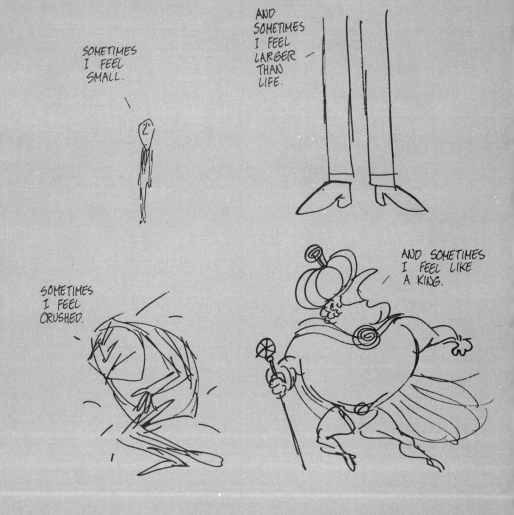

SOMETIMES I FEEL SLOW.

AND
SOMETIMES
I FEEL
LIKE A
WIT.

BUT MOST
OF THE
TIME I —
FEEL JUST
LIKE ME.

SO
I —
DRINK.

YOU KNOW WHEN I WAS A KID I USED TO SEE MOVIES WHERE THIS GUY LIKE PETER LAWFORD WOULD GO TO A PARTY AND HE'D MEET JUNE ALLYSON.

AND HE'D SAY TO HIS BUDDY, EDDIE BRACKEN, "SOMEDAY I'M GOING TO MARRY THAT GIRL." AND HE ALWAYS DID.

AND I THOUGHT THAT WHEN I GREW UP THAT'S THE WAY IT WOULD BE. I'D GO TO A PARTY LIKE THE ONE I MET YOU AT TONIGHT AND I'D SAY- "SOMEDAY I'M GOING TO MARRY THAT GIRL."

HOW VERY SWEET.

I USED TO HAVE THE SAME EXPERIENCE
WITH MOVIES. I ALWAYS LOVED IT
WHEN MELVYN DOUGLAS AND
CONSTANCE BENNETT WOULD MEET
AT A
PARTY—

MELVYN DOUGLAS
AND
CONSTANCE BENNETT?

YES.
AND
HE'D
SAY
TO
RALPH
BELLAMY—

SAY - JUST
HOW OLD
ARE YOU?

EVENTUALLY ONE
REACHES THE
CONCLUSION THAT
COMMERCIAL
ACCEPTANCE
MASS MEDIA-
WISE DOES
NOT NECES-
SARILY MEAN
FULFILLMENT.

SO I DECIDED TO WRITE
A TV PLAY THAT WOULD
BE A **CONTRIBUTION**.
I DECIDED TO
TACKLE **SCHOOL
INTEGRATION**.
AFTER ALL
WHY SHOULD
ED MURROW
BE THE ONLY
ONE TO TAKE
A STAND?

I HAD THIS LITTLE COLORED
BOY (MAYBE SID POITIER)
ENTER A HOSTILE
SOUTHERN SCHOOL
AS ITS FIRST
INTEGRATED
STUDENT. HIS
FATHER (MEL
FERRER), A
HUMBLE MINISTER,
BRINGS HIM TO
CLASS THROUGH
THREATENING
CROWDS.

THE SCHOOL BULLY
(TONY CURTIS) PICKS
A FIGHT BUT THE
COLORED BOY WINS
BECAUSE HE'S A
NATURAL FIGHTER.
A FRIENDSHIP
DEVELOPS. BUT
THEN THE ROMANCE
LANGUAGE TEACHER
(ZSA ZSA GABOR)
IS ASSAULTED.

THE BLAME IS PLACED ON THE COLORED BOY. TONY CURTIS HITCHES TO NEW YORK AND BRINGS BACK A JEWISH LAWYER (BARRY SULLIVAN).

IN THE FINAL COURTROOM SCENE THE LAWYER PLEADS FOR UNDERSTANDING AND PATIENCE ON BOTH SIDES. THE FADE OUT SHOT SHOWS EVERYONE — WHITE AND BLACK ALIKE — REFLECTING FOR THE FIRST TIME ON THEIR **OWN** DEFECTS.

OF COURSE THE NETWORKS WOULDN'T TOUCH IT. THEY MADE ME CHANGE THE COLORED KID TO A WHITE BOY WITH A SPEECH IMPEDIMENT. TAB HUNTER DID IT. JUST GREAT!

THE CRITICS WENT WILD. CALLED IT A SEARCHING ALLEGORY.

IT **MAY** WIN AN "EMMY."

IT HASN'T AND IT WON'T! IT WON'T DO A THING AND I KNEW IT ALL ALONG - IT JUST **WON'T!**

WHAT'S
THE
DIFFERENCE.

AT FIRST I FOUND HIM **AMUSING**. SUCH A **YOUNG** BOY. SO **UNAWARE**. I FELT SORRY FOR HIM.

I TOLD HIM I WAS **FAR** TOO OLD FOR HIM. BUT HE KEPT CALLING. HE BEGGED TO SEE ME. I FELT SORRY FOR HIM.

I REFUSED TO LET HIM PAY MY WAY. I INSISTED WE DO EVERYTHING DUTCH. HE NEVER KNEW HOW TO ARGUE. I FELT SORRY FOR HIM.

HE BEGAN COMING BY AT NIGHT. HE'D BRING BEER AND WE'D SIT AND TALK FOR HOURS, HE WAS SUCH A **BABY**. I FELT SORRY FOR HIM.

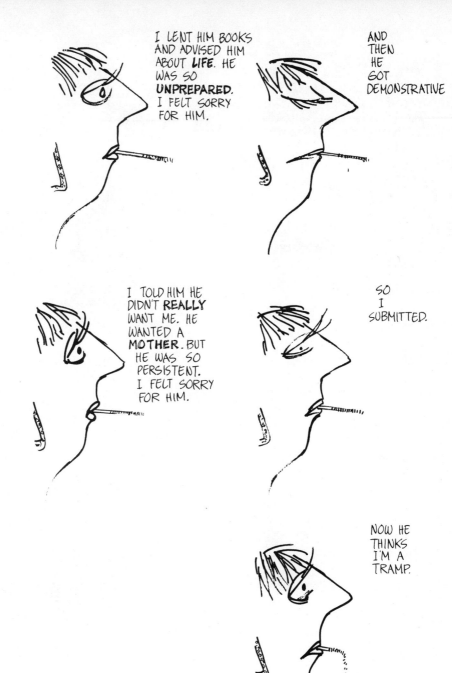

I HAD AN ANSWERING SERVICE ONCE. EVERY DAY I'D CALL UP AND SAY "THIS IS BERNARD MERGENDIELER, ARE THERE ANY MESSAGES?" AND EVERY DAY THE GIRL WOULD ANSWER— "NO MESSAGES, MR. MERGEN-DIELER."

IT WENT ON LIKE THIS FOR **THREE** WEEKS. **EVERY** DAY I'D CALL UP—AND **EVERY** DAY SHE'D ANSWER— "NO MESSAGES, MR. MERGENDIELER."

I GOT **EMBARRASSED** I QUIT CALLING EVERY DAY. SOMETIMES I WOULDN'T CALL **ALL WEEK**— AND ALWAYS SHE'D SAY "NO MESSAGES, MR. MERGENDIELER."

BY THE SIXTH WEEK I DETECTED A NOTE OF **PITY** IN HER VOICE.

DO YOU KNOW WHAT ITS LIKE TO BE **PITIED** BY YOUR **ANSWERING SERVICE**?

SHE BEGAN TO
CALL ME
"BERNIE·BOY"!
I KNEW I
HAD TO DO
SOMETHING!

SO ONE DAY I DIALED MY **OWN**
NUMBER AND I LET IT RING TILL
SHE ANSWERED — AND THEN IN
A DISGUISED VOICE I SAID —
"MAY I SPEAK TO BERNARD
MERGENDIELER — NELSON
ROCKEFELLER HERE"

AND
SHE
BEGAN
TO
CRY.

"OH, GOD BLESS YOU,
MR. ROCKEFELLER"
SHE SAID. "THANK
YOU — THANK YOU —
THANK YOU — "
AND SHE WAS
WEEPING AND
KISSING
THE
PHONE!

THE NEXT
DAY, I
HAD THE
DAMN
THING
TAKEN
OUT.

GO AHEAD! **EAT** ME! PLAY INTO **THEIR** HANDS.

PLEASE. MUST WE CONTINUALLY BICKER? CAN'T WE JUST ACCEPT OUR GIVEN ROLES?

OF COURSE, **YOU'D** SAY THAT. REFUSAL TO CHANGE IS A CHARACTERISTIC OF YOUR CLASS.

LOOK. I'M NOT AGAINST INTELLIGENT CHANGE. BUT THIS QUESTION HAS BEEN LOOKED INTO BEFORE. CATS HAVE **ALWAYS** KILLED MICE. IT'S A TRADITION.

AN OUTMODED RITUAL UNFIT FOR TODAY'S HUMANISTIC VALUES. DON'T YOU SEE WHO PROFITS MOST FROM THE UNNATURAL ENMITY BETWEEN OUR PEOPLES?

YOUR KIND ALWAYS HAS TO LOOK FOR VILLAINS. IT BORES ME.

HOW INCREDIBLY NAIVE! WHOSE ENDS DO YOU **REALLY** SERVE? WHO GAINS BY DIVERTING BOTH OF US INTO A **USELESS** STRUGGLE THAT CAN'T **EVER** END?

;SIGH; I SUPPOSE YOU'LL TELL ME WHETHER I WANT TO HEAR OR NOT.

IT'S **MAN!** YOU SILLY INNOCENT! **MAN!**

OH, COME NOW. MAN PETS ME. MAN GIVES ME FOOD.

NOW I FEEL THERE HAS BEEN AND IS NOW A CERTAIN MISCONSTRUCTION OF SOME REMARKS THAT I HAVE MADE — WAS QUOTED TO HAVE MADE, HERE, AT THIS CON- FERENCE, LAST WEEK.

NOW I WANT TO, BECAUSE ITS ALWAYS BEEN MY POLICY, TO CLEAR THIS THING UP RIGHT AWAY.

I INTENDED NO SLUR OR DISRESPECT AT ALL TO THE MEMORY OF BABY FACE NELSON.

YOU KNOW IT IS MY POLICY TO NEVER DEAL IN PERSONALITIES! IN MY REFER- ENCES TO MR. NELSON I REFERRED ONLY TO THE LEGEND, SO TO SPEAK — A FIC- TITIOUS CHARACTER YOU MIGHT SAY —

— LIKE WILD BILL HICKOK OR MR. NIXON

NOW I HAVE NO IDEA WHERE BABY FACE NELSON, IN FACT, STOOD ON THE INTE- GRATION ISSUE OR, FOR THAT MATTER, ON THE BLOWING UP OF SCHOOLS AND SYNAGOGUES. LET ME MAKE THAT CLEAR.

I WANT TO CORRECT ANY MISUNDERSTANDING ON THIS POINT BECAUSE I DEPLORE THE ACTIONS OF EXTREMISTS ON BOTH SIDES— THOSE WHO BLOW UP SCHOOLS AND THOSE WHO WANT TO KEEP THEM OPEN. I CAN'T STRESS THAT TOO FIRMLY!

I THINK IF THOSE PEOPLE WHO WANT TO BLOW UP THINGS THOUGHT ABOUT FAIR PLAY FOR AWHILE THEY WOULD SEE THERE ARE DIFFERENT WAYS OF PLAYING THE GAME, SO TO SPEAK AND FINAL- IZING THEIR GOALS. WHY DON'T THEY GO THROUGH THE COURTS?

NOW DO NOT MISUNDERSTAND. THIS IS NOT MEANT TO BE AN INDORSEMENT OF THE COURTS. I HAVE NEVER TAKEN A STAND ON THE COURTS. I THINK IN MY POSITION THAT WOULD BE UNCALLED FOR BECAUSE, AND I FEEL STRONGLY ABOUT THIS, I THINK THIS ISSUE LIKE FOREIGN AFFAIRS— —SHOULD BE ABOVE PARTISAN DEBATE SO AS NOT TO GIVE OUR ENEMIES THE WRONG IMPRESSION, WHATEVER THAT MAY BE.

I MEAN, OF COURSE, NO DISRESPECT FOR OUR ENEMIES BY THAT REMARK.

NEXT QUESTION.

MY FATHER SAYS THAT "THANK GOD, IT'S A BLESSING WE DON'T LIVE IN THE SOUTH WITH ALL THIS GOING ON."

ABSOLUTELY. MY FATHER AGREES.

MY FATHER SAYS, "HA! AND THEY CALL THIS A **DEMOCRACY!** DON'T THEY KNOW HOW THIS LOOKS TO THE UNCOMMITTED COUNTRIES?"

EXACTLY WHAT MY FATHER SAYS. MY FATHER IS VERY INTERESTED IN UNCOMMITTED COUNTRIES.

MY FATHER SAYS, "I'M ASHAMED TO CALL MYSELF AN AMERICAN WITH LITTLE ROCK AND ALL."

MY FATHER QUITE DEFINITELY AGREES. HE'S ALWAYS BEING ASHAMED OF CALLING HIMSELF AN AMERICAN.

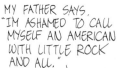

MY FATHER SAYS THAT, "THANK GOD THERE'S NONE OF THIS NONSENSE HERE IN NEW YORK."

MY FATHER GOES RIGHT ALONG WITH YOUR FATHER. THEY CAN THROW THE REST OF THE COUNTRY AWAY AS FAR AS MY FATHER IS CONCERNED.

WHERE DO THEY SEND YOU?

THORSTEIN VEBLEN ACADEMY IN SCARSDALE. HOW ABOUT YOU?

THE PANDIT NEHRU SCHOOL. IT'S IN RYE.

YOU LOOK SENSATIONAL, DOROTHY.

I DON'T LOOK SENSATIONAL. I'M JUST GOOD AT **MAKING** MYSELF LOOK SENSATIONAL. HE MUST BE **BLIND**.

AND YOU'RE **FUN TO BE** WITH. I'VE NEVER KNOWN ANYONE WHO WAS SO MUCH FUN TO **BE** WITH.

HE PRACTICALLY DOESN'T KNOW I'M **AROUND** SO I'M FUN TO **BE** WITH. IF HE KNEW WHO THE HELL I TRULY WAS I WOULDN'T BE SUCH FUN TO **BE** WITH.

YOU KNOW YOU REALLY BROKE ME UP AT THE MOVIE WITH THAT REFERENCE TO JOHN WAYNE AND DESCARTES. **GOD**, WHAT A SENSE OF HUMOR!

THAT'S NOT **HUMOR** THAT'S **SNOB WIT** HOW **EASY** HE IS TO BE BRITTLE FOR.

ONE DAY HE COMES HOME- HE SAYS -" MAMMA . I AM NOT WELL EMOTIONALLY. I NEED A PSYCHIATRIST. "

SO I SEND HIM TO A PSYCHIATRIST. AFTER ALL IF YOU CAN'T HELP YOUR OWN SON, WHAT'S A MOTHER FOR ?

SO ONE DAY HE COMES HOME. HE SAYS -"MAMMA, PSYCHOANALYSIS HAS TAUGHT ME THAT HOME IS A SMOTHERING INFLUENCE. I'M MOVING OUT. "

SO I FIND HIM HIS OWN APARTMENT. AFTER ALL IF YOU CAN'T HELP YOUR OWN SON, WHAT'S A MOTHER FOR ?

I GIVE HIM RENT MONEY. I GIVE HIM PSYCHIATRIST MONEY. I GIVE HIM A LITTLE EXTRA SO HE COULD ENJOY HIMSELF. LISTEN - WHAT WOULD I DO WITH IT? WHAT'S A MOTHER FOR ?

SO ONE DAY HE CALLS UP. HE SAYS - "MAMMA, YOU ARE GIVING ME ALL THIS MONEY JUST SO I SHOULD FEEL **GUILTY!** GUILT IS A MOTHER'S WEAPON.

ALLRIGHT, WHY ARGUE? WHAT DOES IT GET YOU? SO I STOP PAYING HIS PSYCHIATRIST AND I STOP PAYING HIS RENT AND I STOP GIVING HIM ANYTHING EXTRA.

SO NOW ITS OVER A MONTH - HE'S DISPOSSESSED, HE CAN'T FIND A JOB. HIS PSYCHIATRIST IS SU'ING HIM.

BUT LISTEN - SO LONG AS HE'S HAPPY.

SO I WAS STANDING ON THE CORNER WAITING FOR SOMEBODY TO CROSS ME BECAUSE I'M NOT ALLOWED TO CROSS BY MYSELF.

AND THIS LADY COMES BY AND SHE SAYS- "HERE IS A BUBBLE GUM SAMPLE. DO YOU CHEW THIS BRAND?"

AND I SAYS-"I DON'T **LIKE** BUBBLE GUM". SO THIS LADY TAKES OUT A PAD AND SHE STARTS WRITING AND THEN SHE SAYS-"WHY DON'T YOU LIKE IT? IS IT THE DESIGN OF THE WRAPPER?"

AND I SAYS - "NO IT'S 'CAUSE I CAN'T BLOW BUBBLES."

SO SHE WRITES THAT DOWN ON HER PAD AND THEN SHE SAYS- "HOW WOULD YOU LIKE A BUBBLE GUM WHICH WAS GUARANTEED TO BLOW BUBBLES?"

AND I SAYS - "I DON'T KNOW- I CAN'T WHISTLE THROUGH MY FINGERS EITHER."

"AND I CAN'T CROSS THE STREET BY MYSELF AND MY TEACHERS SAY I DON'T TRY –"

"AND WHEN WE PLAY GAMES I'M ALWAYS 'IT' AND I'M NEVER ALLOWED TO WATCH WHAT I WANT AND MY FATHER KEEPS CALLING ME BY MY OLDER SISTER'S NAME –"

AND ALL OF A SUDDEN I'M CRYING LIKE MAD AND THIS LADY IS WRITING AWAY ON HER PAD AND SHE'S CRYING TOO –

AND I SAY – "SO YOU SEE – IT HAS **NOTHING** TO DO WITH YOUR BUBBLE GUM! **IT'S ME! IT'S ALL ME!**"

AND I'M SHOUTING AND CRYING AND THE LADY IS WRITING AWAY AND A CROWD COMES ALONG.

AND SOME BIG GUY SAYS – "IS THIS LADY BOTHERING YOU, GIRLIE?" AND THE CROWD TURNS UGLY.

SO THE LADY GETS VERY NERVOUS AND SHE STARTS HANDING OUT BUBBLE GUM TO EVERYBODY AND SHE DROPS HER PAD IN THE STREET –

AND SHE'S ASKING EVERYBODY – "WHY DON'T YOU LIKE IT? IS IT THE DESIGN OF THE WRAPPER?" AND NOBODY KNOWS WHAT SHE'S TALKING ABOUT.

SO THEN I WENT HOME.

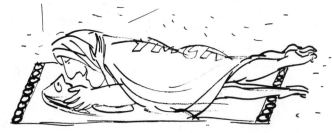

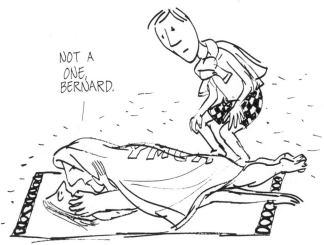

A
DANCE
TO
THE ~
END
OF
SUMMER.

IN THIS
DANCE
I HAVE
SYMBOLIZED
THE
SUMMER ~
SOLSTICE
IN ITS
DECLENSION.

THE
TIDES-
THE
SAND- ~
THE
SEA-

THE SUMMER
FLOWERS -
THE SAND
PIPERS -
THE GOOD
FISHERFOLK.

INSECT
REPELLENT,
THE MAIN
BOARDWALK,
BABY OIL.

ALL ARE GATHERED
IN AN ORGANIC
UNITY. ALL
TESTIFY TO
MAN AND
NATURE
BEING
AS ONE.

WHAT'S
SHE
DOING
THAT
FOR?

TO
LOSE
WEIGHT.

AND NOW THAT GREAT NEW FUN GAME THAT'S SWEEPING AMERICA— "RECANTATION"!

APPLAUSE

CLAP CLAP CLAP. CLAP CLAP

"RECANTATION" THE SHOW THAT ASKS THE QUESTION "WHAT MORAL STRUGGLE HAVE YOU GONE THROUGH?" WHO'S OUR FIRST GUEST, BOB?

HI, OUR FIRST GUEST IS MR. C.L. OF DES MOINES, IOWA.

DES MOINES, IOWA! HOW ABOUT THAT, AUDIENCE? CLAP CLAP CLAP. AND WHAT IS YOUR RECANTATION, MR. C.L. OF DES MOINES?

I'M A LABOR RACKETEER, A COMMUN- IST AND AN ATOMIC SPY. I JUST HAD TO COME

GOD BLESS YOU FOR FACING UP TO IT, MR. C.L. OF DES MOINES, IOWA!

IT WASN'T EASY. I THOUGHT A LOT ABOUT IT. I WON'T BORE YOU WITH THE MORAL STRUGGLE I WENT THROUGH.

AND WHAT FINALLY PROMPTED YOUR DECISION, MR. C.L. OF DES MOINES, IOWA?

I GOT A LETTER FROM MY LITTLE DOG CHECKERS. "C.L. OF DES MOINES," IT READ. "TELL THE TRUTH." I WON'T BORE YOU WITH THE MORAL STRUGGLE CHECKERS WENT THROUGH BEFORE HE WROTE THAT LETTER.

GOD BLESS **THAT DOG**
AND **HIS LETTER!** HOW
ABOUT THAT AUDIENCE?
DON'T WE GOD BLESS
THAT DOG AND HIS
LETTER?

CLAP CLAP CLAP CLAP

THAT'S WHY **I HAD** TO COME HERE. NOT
JUST FOR **ME**. BUT FOR ALL THOSE
OTHERS ALL OVER AMERICA WHO, IN
ONE UNGUARDED MOMENT, MAY SLIP
INTO BEING A LABOR RACKETEER, A
COMMUNIST AND AN ATOMIC SPY.

YOU HAVE
DONE A
PUBLIC
SERVICE,
MR. C.L.
OF DES
MOINES,
IOWA.

HI, WE HAVE JUST RECEIVED A
CALL ON OUR HEART LINE FROM
THE ATTORNEY GENERAL. HE
SAYS "GOD BLESS YOU, MR. C.L.
OF DES MOINES, IOWA. WE
WON'T PROSECUTE. ARE YOU
AND
CHECKERS
FREE
FOR
DINNER
NEXT
THURSDAY?"

DID YOU **HEAR**
THAT, AUDIENCE?
**LET'S GOD
BLESS THAT
ATTORNEY
GENERAL!**

CLAP CLAP CLAP
CLAP PHTW WEET!

THANK YOU, MR. C.L. OF DES MOINES
FOR FACING UP TO **YOUR** MORAL
STRUGGLE. THIS IS HI STANDARD
SAYING GOODBYE TILL NEXT WEEK
WITH THIS ONE REMINDER—"**ARE
ANY OF US TRULY CLEAN?**"

APPLA·

CLAP CLAP CLAP
CLAP CLAP CLAP

I DON'T
GET
AROUSED
ANYMORE.

NOR DO I
NOR DO I

SAY
SOMETHING
TO
AROUSE
ME.

MISSILE MADNESS!

MISSILE MADNESS.
YES, THAT'S A
GOOD ONE. THAT
CERTAINLY SHOULD
HAVE AROUSED
ME. BUT NO IT
DOESN'T.

ATOMIC HOLOCAUST!

AH, THAT USED
TO BE A VERY
EFFECTIVE ONE.
YEARS AGO I
GOT AROUSED
ALL THE TIME
ON ATOMIC
HOLOCAUST.
BUT NOW—.

**BRINKS-
MANSHIP!
ROCKET
DIPLOMACY!
INDIA!
BERLIN!**

VERY GOOD. VERY GOOD.
FOR A MOMENT THERE
I ALMOST FELT AROUSED.
I GUESS IT'S BECAUSE
THEY'RE SO CURRENT.

DO YOU THINK
WE'VE TURNED
APATHETIC?

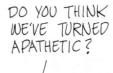

APATHY IS SUCH A
BAD WORD. I'D HATE
TO THINK IT'S
APATHY WE SUFFER
FROM.

LETS JUST
CALL IT
FAITH.

LISTEN, IF KHRUSHCHEV WANTS A PICTURE OF AMERICA LET HIM COME TO **MY** HOME.

IF KHRUSHCHEV WANTS TO KNOW HOW **SELFISH** YOUR OWN **FLESH** AND **BLOOD** CAN BE LET HIM HAVE A CONVERSATION WITH MY DAUGHTER. **TAKE! TAKE! TAKE!** EVEN **HE** WOULDN'T BELIEVE IT.

MY HUSBAND WILL TELL HIM. IF KHRUSHCHEV WANTS TO KNOW HOW **NOT** TO DO **ANYTHING** TO HELP HIS FAMILY LET HIM TALK TO MY HUSBAND.

—OR MY SON. LET HIM MEET MY SON! KHRUSHCHEV WOULD GET DOWN ON HIS **HANDS** AND **KNEES** TO ME AND **BEG** MY FORGIVENESS. THAT **HE** SHOULD GIVE ME **MORE** WORRIES WITH THE KIND OF SON I'VE GOT.

LISTEN, IF KHRUSHCHEV IS COMING FOR ADVICE, I COULD GIVE HIM **ALL** HE NEEDS. IT WOULD SOLVE ALL THE WORLD'S PROBLEMS.

JUST NEVER BE A MOTHER.

I ALWAYS WANTED A SON NAMED "ADAM."

WHO KNOWS WHY.

WHEN WE GOT MARRIED I TOLD MY WIFE - OUR FIRST SON IS GOING TO BE AN "ADAM."

SHE SAID FINE. SHE SAID FINE.

SO WE HAD A SON AND MY WIFE'S SIDE OF THE FAMILY SAID - "ADAM"? WHAT KIND OF NAME IS "ADAM"? SO WE NAMED IT "HERBERT."

AFTER HER FATHER.

WELL, WHAT'S DONE IS DONE. BUT OUR **SECOND** SON I WAS **DETER-MINED** TO HAVE NAMED "ADAM."

WHO KNOWS WHY.

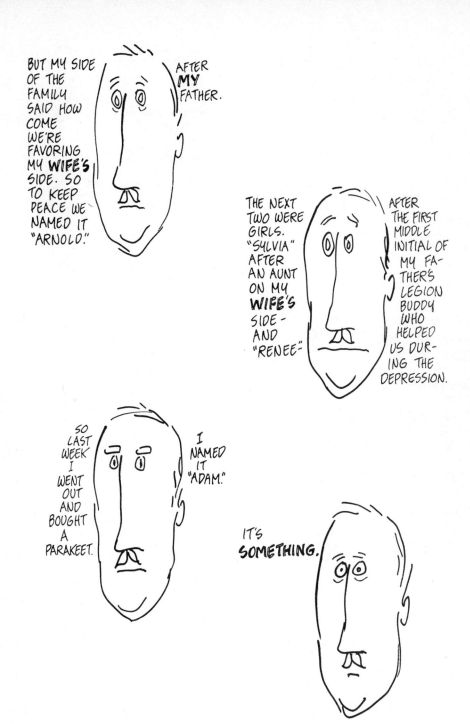

BUT MY SIDE OF THE FAMILY SAID HOW COME WE'RE FAVORING MY **WIFE'S** SIDE. SO TO KEEP PEACE WE NAMED IT "ARNOLD."

AFTER **MY** FATHER.

THE NEXT TWO WERE GIRLS. "SYLVIA" AFTER AN AUNT ON MY **WIFE'S** SIDE - AND "RENEE."

AFTER THE FIRST MIDDLE INITIAL OF MY FA-THER'S LEGION BUDDY WHO HELPED US DUR-ING THE DEPRESSION.

SO LAST WEEK I WENT OUT AND BOUGHT A PARAKEET.

I NAMED IT "ADAM."

IT'S **SOMETHING.**

MY
TROUBLE
IS
I'M
NAMED
"BERNARD."

WHO MADE IT
MY NAME? DID
I MAKE IT MY
NAME? I DON'T
FEEL LIKE A
BERNARD. I
HAD HOSTILE
PARENTS AND
THEY NAMED
ME "BERNARD."
IS THAT **MY**
FAULT?

O.K. - BERNARD IS
FINE FOR OTHER
PEOPLE BUT ALL
MY LIFE WHEN I
WAS OUT ON THE
STREET AND
PEOPLE CALLED
ME "BERNARD."
I THOUGHT
THEY WERE
SPEAKING TO
SOMEBODY
ELSE.

AND WHEN I REALIZED
IT WAS **ME** I FELT
DISAPPOINTED.

I JUST DON'T **IDENTIFY** WITH THE NAME! INSIDE I'M ALL DIFFERENT FROM A "BERNARD." IF YOU KNEW ME ON THE INSIDE YOU WOULDN'T RECOGNIZE ME FROM KNOWING ME ON THE OUTSIDE.

YOU SHOULD SEE ME WHEN I'M BY MYSELF! THE **ME** ON THE INSIDE BEGINS TO **FLOWER** AND **COME ALIVE!** AND THEN SOMEBODY COMES ALONG AND SAYS "BERNARD" AND IT REMEMBERS WHO I AM AND GETS **CRUSHED.**

I KNOW I WOULD BE DIFFERENT IF PEOPLE ONLY CALLED ME BY MY **INSIDE** NAME –

"SPIKE."

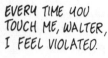

EVERY TIME YOU TOUCH ME, WALTER, I FEEL VIOLATED.

THATS VERY TRUE TO FORM. SHALL I TELL YOU WHY?

OTHER BOYS CAN KISS ME - EVEN PET ME AND I DON'T MIND. BUT WITH YOU I **MIND**, WALTER. **GOD, DO I MIND!**

OF COURSE YOU'D MIND. BEING WHAT YOU ARE YOU'D **HAVE** TO MIND. SHALL I TELL YOU WHY?

I THINK I'D JUST AS SOON HAVE YOU LEAVE.

ITS BECAUSE YOU **KNOW** YOU CAN **HANDLE** THOSE OTHERS. YOU **KNOW** THEY'RE **HARMLESS**.

I'M NOT SURE I'M INTERESTED IN YOUR OPINIONS, WALTER.

BUT **I'M** NOT HARMLESS AND YOU **KNOW** IT.

I USED TO BE A SHORT ORDER COOK IN A DINER.

ALL NIGHT LONG THESE ODD BALLS WOULD COME IN — ALWAYS CARRYIN' BOOKS — ALWAYS ORDERING TOASTED ENGLISH AND WATER. I MEAN A LITTLE WEIRD BUT NICE. AND WE'D TALK A LOT. SO ANYHOW THEY'D ALWAYS ASK ME WHAT I DID **BEFORE** —

AND I'D TELL 'EM ABOUT PUNCHING CATTLE IN TEXAS AND MINING SILVER IN COLORADO AND MY FRUIT PICKING DAYS IN MEXICO AND BEING A TRUCK DRIVER AND A MERCHANT MARINE. AND ALL THESE STRANGE TYPES WOULD SIT THERE, LISTENING AND THEY'D SAY "**CRAZY — YEAH CRAZY**."

SO ONE DAY, BY ACCIDENT, I TAKE A LOOK AT THE BOOKS THEY'RE ALWAYS CARRYIN' AND ON THE BACKS ARE THESE PICTURES OF THE GUYS WHO WROTE THEM AND THEY ALL NEED HAIR CUTS AND THEY'RE WEARING ARMY FIELD JACKETS AND UNDER THE PICTURES IT TELLS WHAT THEY ALL USED TO BE —

COWBOYS,
SILVER MINERS,
FRUIT PICKERS IN
MEXICO,
TRUCK DRIVERS,
MERCHANT MARINES,
AND SHORT ORDER
COOKS. SO THAT'S
HOW I GOT **WISE**.
WHY SHOULDN'T
I MAKE SOME
MONEY?

SO I PUT ON MY ARMY FIELD
JACKET AND I GO SEE THIS
PUBLISHER. AND I TELL
HIM I USED TO BE A
COWBOY, A SILVER
MINER, A FRUIT PICKER
IN MEXICO, A TRUCK
DRIVER, A MERCHANT
MARINE AND A
SHORT ORDER
COOK.

SO HE
GAVE ME
A
$2,000
ADVANCE.

AND
THAT'S
HOW I
BOUGHT
THIS
DINER.

ONE OF
THESE DAYS
THEY'LL
CATCH UP
WITH
ME.

MR. SANTA CLAUS, I UNDERSTAND YOU ARE GIVING 20% MORE GIFTS **THIS** YEAR THAN **LAST**. DO YOU FEEL THAT THIS IS HEALTHY, SIR, OR THAT IT MIGHT NOT BE LOOKED UPON BY THE PEOPLE AS AN ANNUAL DOLE?

YES. NOW THAT'S AN IFFY QUESTION. NOW I WANT TO MAKE MY FEELINGS KNOWN ON THIS POINT- THE PARTICULAR POINT YOU ARE BRINGING UP HERE BECAUSE IF WE ARE ALL TO UNDERSTAND THIS THING IT IS IMPORTANT TO DISCUSS IT OUT IN THE OPEN-

NOW- LET ME MAKE THIS POINT- IT IS **ONE** THING TO HAVE WHAT YOU CALL A DOLE AND IT IS **ANOTHER** THING TO SPUR THE ECONOMY BY SETTING AN EXAMPLE OF GIVING - TO THUS INSPIRE GIVING IN OTHERS AND THAT IS WHAT WE INTEND TO DO HERE AND THAT MAKES ALL THE DIFFERENCE IN THE YOU MIGHT SAY WORLD.

THEN, SIR YOU ARE IN FAVOR OF GROUP GIVING?

NOW, LET ME MAKE MYSELF CLEAR. NOW IF SEPARATE PEOPLE DECIDE TO GIVE ALL ON THEIR OWN - MIND YOU- AND THEY FOLLOW THIS EXAMPLE THAT I HAVE TALKED ABOUT HERE WHY THAT IS ALL TO THE GOOD.

BUT IF THEY JOIN TOGETHER INTO WHAT YOU MIGHT CALL A GROUP- A GROUP THAT GIVES - A **PURCHASING CONSPIRACY**- WELL I DON'T KNOW IF THAT PLAYS INTO OUR TRADITIONS- ESPECIALLY AT **THIS** TIME OF YEAR.

SIR, DO YOU THINK GROUP GIVING WILL ENCOURAGE THE SPENDERS?

NOW I HAVE SAID TO YOU PEOPLE **TIME AND AGAIN** THAT SPENDING WITH AN EYE TOWARD SAVING IS ALL TO THE GOOD.

YOU CAN'T **GIVE** WITHOUT **SPENDING.** **IF ANYONE KNOWS HOW TO DO IT I WISH THEY'D TELL ME!** IT'S THE **KIND** OF SPENDING - THAT KIND I CONTINUALLY REFER TO - WHICH IS AGAINST OUR BEST INTERESTS AND TRADITIONS THAT **I** AM AGAINST.

SIR, YOU HAVE EXPRESSED YOUR-SELF ELOQUENTLY ON GIVING. HOW DO YOU FEEL ABOUT **RECEIVING?**

NOW MANY PEOPLE THINK THIS IS A **TOUCHY** SUBJECT WITH ME. (chuckle)

HA HA HA
HA HA
HA

BUT I DON'T WANT YOU PEOPLE TO THINK THAT JUST BECAUSE I STRESS **GIVING,** I AM OPPOSED TO **RE-CEIVING.** NOTHING COULD BE FURTHER FROM THE TRUTH. RECEIVING IS WELL WITHIN THE TRAD-ITIONS OF THIS COUNTRY. THE PIONEERS RECEIVED THE WEST FROM THE INDIANS AND SO ON -

SIR, HOW WOULD YOU DESCRIBE YOUR ROLE?

NOW, I WANT TO STRESS THIS POINT, I DO NOT, NOR DO THE DEPARTMENT STORE PEOPLE WHO APPOINTED ME, CONSIDER MYSELF TO BE A **PARTISAN** SANTA CLAUS.

NOW THE ROLE OF SANTA CLAUS MUST CHANGE AS TRADITION AND THE NEEDS OF THE PEOPLE CHANGE. SO AT ONE POINT HE IS SAINT NICHOLAS- AT ANOTHER HE IS FATHER CHRISTMAS - AND WHAT **I** AM - WHAT I INTEND TO BE AS LONG AS **I** HOLD THIS OFFICE IS SANTA CLAUS NOT FOR ONE GROUP OR ANOTHER, BUT SANTA CLAUS FOR **ALL** THE PEOPLE.

YOU DON'T WISH TO OFFEND ANY GROUPS, SIR?

YOU MIGHT SAY I AM A CONSUMER-WISE ANSWER TO CHRIST.

BUT THEN I SAW THE **EMPTINESS** OF LIFE THE WAY IT WAS. SELF INDULGENCE **IS** EMPTINESS. I DON'T KNOW IF YOU REALIZE THAT. HEY, ARE YOU ALRIGHT?

NO — YES — I MEAN YES.

NOW I'M OFF SELF INDULGENCE. NOW I THINK OF THE GRAND DESIGN AND HOW WE **ALL** FIT IN. ITS GIVEN ME **BELIEF.** ITS MADE ME CONSCIOUS OF LIFE AROUND ME. I WON'T BE HURT IF YOU TELL ME I'M BORING YOU.

NO NO NO

I'D LIKE TO EXPLAIN THE WHOLE IDEA. IT MIGHT HELP YOU IN YOUR **OWN** STRUGGLES. I ONLY WISH SOMEBODY HAD COME TO **ME** YEARS AGO AND— BUT YOU MUST BE **TERRIBLY** TIRED.

WELL. AS A MATTER OF FACT.

YOU SURE I WON'T BE BORING YOU?

OH NO. OH GOD NO.